ICE AGE 3
DAWN OF THE DINOSAURS

Popcorn
ELT
Readers

Meet ...
the animals from

ICE AGE 3
DAWN OF THE DINOSAURS

Manny, Sid and Diego are friends.
They live in a valley in the ice age.
They had a lot of adventures before.

Sid is a sloth. He
is slow but he is
very funny.

Sid

Manny and Ellie are
mammoths. Ellie is going
to have a baby very soon.

Ellie

Manny

Crash and Eddie

Crash and Eddie are possums. They like playing games.

Buck

Buck is a weasel. Buck likes fighting Rudy. But who or what is Rudy?

Dinosaurs

The last **dinosaurs** were here 65,000,000 years ago. But were they the last?

Diego

Diego is a sabre-toothed tiger. He loves adventures.

Before you read ... What do you think? Who is going to have an adventure?

3

New Words

What do these new words mean? Ask your teacher or use your dictionary.

climb

She is **climbing**.

adventure

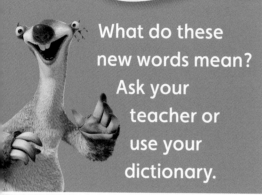

I want to have an **adventure**.

eggs

These are **eggs**.

cave

Look at this **cave**.

escape

The man is **escaping**.

fight

The boys are **fighting**.

ice

The **ice** is very cold.

valley

The house is in a **valley**.

volcano

A **volcano** is very hot.

'What's the matter?'

What's the matter?

The last **ice age** ended about 10,000 years ago.

Verbs

Present	Past
fall	fell
fight	fought
take	took

CHAPTER 1
Diego goes away

It was a beautiful sunny day in the valley. Manny was happy.

'I'm going to be a father soon,' he said.

But his friend Diego was quiet.

'What's the matter, Diego?' Manny asked.

'I'm not good with babies, Manny,' Diego said. 'I'm going away. I want some new adventures!'

When Diego went away, Manny was angry.

'Diego doesn't want to see our baby,' he said to Ellie.

But Sid was sad. 'Ellie and Manny are going to have a baby, but I have no children,' he thought.

He looked for some new friends, but he fell into a big cave in the ice. Suddenly he found three big eggs. He took the eggs and put faces on them.

'These eggs are my children now,' he thought.

Manny and Ellie saw Sid with the eggs.

'Sid, these aren't your eggs,' Manny said. 'The eggs have a mother. She's going to be angry!'

'OK ... I can find their mother,' Sid said.

But Sid didn't want to find the mother. That night, it started to rain. Sid was tired and he wanted to sleep. He put the eggs in a small cave.

'Sleep now my babies,' he said. 'See you in the morning!'

CHAPTER 2
Where's Sid?

In the morning, Sid opened his eyes slowly. He looked at the eggs. They were open.

'Where are my babies?' he said.

Then he saw three funny babies. They were not baby sloths or mammoths or possums, but Sid loved them.

Suddenly there was a terrible noise.

'What's that?' Manny shouted.

A big dinosaur walked into the valley. The dinosaur was a mother. She wanted her babies.

'Help!' shouted Sid.

Sid took the babies to his cave, but the dinosaur found them. She took the babies. Then she took Sid!

'Stop!' shouted Ellie.

Diego was near the cave. There was a terrible noise.

'What's that?' Diego said. He went to see.

'Help!' someone shouted.

'That's Sid!' Diego thought. Then he saw a dinosaur. She had some babies – and she had Sid!

'I must help Sid,' Diego thought. He ran after the dinosaur, but she was very fast.

'I'm going to look for Sid,' Manny said to Ellie. 'You stay here. It's dangerous for the baby.'

'But Sid is my friend too!' Ellie said. 'I'm coming with you.'

'We're coming too!' Crash and Eddie shouted.

They all ran after the dinosaur. They came to a big dark cave in the ice. They climbed down and down. Where was the dinosaur?

CHAPTER 3
A different valley

When they came out of the cave, they were in a different valley. It wasn't cold. Suddenly they saw Diego.

'Diego, what are you doing here?' Manny asked.

'I saw a dinosaur with Sid. I came to find him,' Diego said.

'We're looking for him too!' Ellie said.

In the valley there were dinosaurs everywhere.

'I thought that dinosaurs lived a long time ago!' Diego said.

'But there are some in this valley!' Ellie said. 'And they are big!'

'Help!' Eddie shouted. 'They want to eat us!'

Then they saw a small, brown animal.

'Don't be frightened! Buck is here!' the animal said.

'I'm not frightened. This is exciting!' Diego said.

'Why are you here?' Buck asked. 'It's very dangerous!'

'We're looking for our friend, Sid,' Manny said.

'I can help you,' Buck said. 'Come with me!'

'I don't want to go with you,' Manny shouted.

'These dinosaurs want us for dinner!' Ellie said.
'We're going with Buck!'

'OK,' Manny said unhappily.

'Let's go,' Buck said. 'But don't go near Rudy!'

'Who's Rudy?' Manny asked, but Buck didn't
answer.

Sid was not far away. He was with his babies and the mother dinosaur. She was kind to Sid.

The baby dinosaurs could run quickly. Sid couldn't run fast so he climbed on the mother dinosaur.

'This is fun,' he said. But then he fell off.

'Wait for me!' he shouted. But the mother and her babies didn't hear.

CHAPTER 4
A new mammoth

A big dinosaur saw Sid. It was hungry. Sid ran and ran. He escaped, but he fell into a volcano.

'Help!' he shouted, but no one could hear. 'I never said goodbye to my babies,' he thought sadly. 'I'm not going to see them again. And I'm not going to see my friends again.'

Suddenly Ellie stopped. 'Oh no!' she said.

'We mustn't stop here,' Buck said. 'Look! All those small dinosaurs want to eat us.'

'My baby is coming!' Ellie said.

'We have to stay here,' said Manny.

'Manny and I can fight the dinosaurs,' Diego shouted. 'Go and look for Sid!'

'OK. Let's go!' Buck said to Crash and Eddie.

Diego and Manny fought and fought. It was very dangerous but they didn't stop. Soon there were no more small dinosaurs.

'Thanks, Diego,' Ellie said. 'Manny, look! Here's our baby mammoth!'

Buck, Crash and Eddie looked for Sid.
'Let's fly!' Buck said. 'It's faster.'
They went up and up. They could see dinosaurs everywhere. They could see everything in the valley.

'Look! There's Sid in the volcano!' Eddie said.

'Help!' Sid shouted.

'Don't be frightened!' Buck shouted.

'Buck is here!' Crash and Eddie said.

They went down and down into the volcano.

'Jump on!' they shouted to Sid, and they all went back to see Ellie.

'Oh, Sid!' Diego said. 'It is good to see you!'

'Look!' Ellie said. 'This is Peaches, our new baby!'

'Oh, she's beautiful!' Sid said.

CHAPTER 5
Escape from Rudy

The animals looked at the new baby. They were very happy. But suddenly there was a terrible noise.

'Oh no! What's that?' Diego shouted.

Then they saw it. It was big. It was horrible.

'It's Rudy!' Buck said. 'But ...'

'Don't be frightened! Buck is here!' everyone shouted.

Rudy was very strong and very dangerous. He was the biggest dinosaur in the valley – and he was hungry.

All the friends fought Rudy and he fell down. 'We must escape now!' shouted Buck. 'Quick!' But Rudy was up again and he was next to Sid. 'Help!' Sid shouted. 'Rudy is going to eat me!'

Suddenly Sid saw the mother dinosaur. Rudy was very big, but the mother dinosaur was angry. She wanted to help Sid.

She ran at Rudy and Rudy fell into a big valley.

'That's the end of Rudy!' Buck said. 'What am I going to do now?'

'Come home with us,' Ellie said.

'Goodbye, mum!' Sid said sadly. 'Goodbye, babies! Let's go home!'

The animals walked and walked.

Suddenly there was a terrible noise far away.

'That's Rudy! I'm going to stay here!' Buck said. 'I must stop him.'

Manny looked at Diego.

'Are you going to stay too, Diego?' he asked. 'It's exciting here.'

'No, thanks,' said Diego. 'I want to go home. I always have the best adventures with my friends!'

The End

Real World

DINOSAURS

The last dinosaurs lived 65,000,000 years ago. So how do we know about them? And were they similar to any animals today?

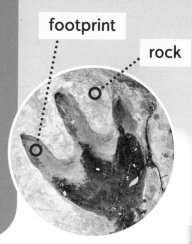

footprint

rock

Footprints

We know about dinosaurs because people find skeletons and footprints in rocks and caves.

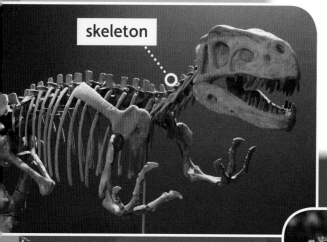

skeleton

lizard

Reptiles

Dinosaurs were very big reptiles. Reptiles are animals with cold blood, for example, lizards. They don't like the cold. They sit in the sun to keep warm. Some reptiles sleep in winter.

★
What other reptiles do you know?
★

Dinosaurs and birds

Dinosaurs made nests and had eggs. Some dinosaurs also had feathers. Some birds today are similar to dinosaurs, for example, the ostrich.

nest

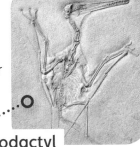

ostrich

But dinosaurs couldn't fly. At the same time as the dinosaurs, there were other reptiles that could fly, for example, pterodactyls.

skeleton of a pterodactyl

Did you know?

🐾 The biggest dinosaurs were more than 30 metres long and 15 metres tall.

🐾 Tyrannosaurus Rex was one of the most dangerous dinosaurs. People call it 'T-Rex'.

🐾 One of the smallest dinosaurs, compsognathus, was only about 65 centimetres long.

What do these words mean? Find out.

similar   blood   keep warm   birds   feathers

After you read

1 Who said it? Match the names and the sentences.

a) Manny   i) 'Goodbye, babies!'

b) Diego   ii) 'My baby is coming!'

c) Sid   iii) 'It's dangerous for the baby.'

d) Buck   iv) 'Why are you here?'

e) Ellie   v) 'This is exciting!'

2 Complete the sentences about Diego's adventure.

A big mummy **1** *dinosaur* took Sid away.
2 .... and I went to look for Sid.
We went to a different **3** *world*.
There were a lot of **4** *dinosaurs*.
We made a new friend. He was a weasel
and his name was **5** *Buck*.
We found Sid in a **6** *volcano*!
There was a very big horrible dinosaur.
His name was **7** *Rudy*.
Ellie had her **8** *baby*. Her name is Peaches.

Where's the popcorn?
Look in your book.
Can you find it?

Puzzle time!

1 Put the letters in order. Then match the words and the pictures.

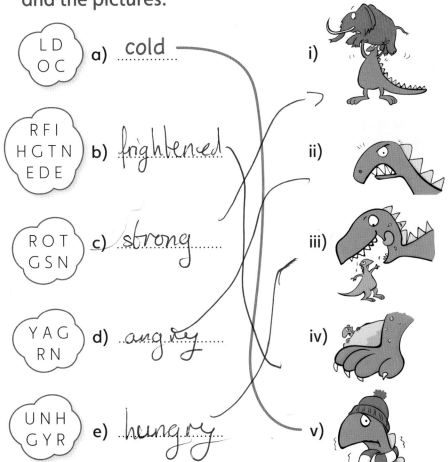

LD O C   a) cold

RFI HGTN EDE   b) frightened

ROT GSN   c) strong

YAG RN   d) angry

UNH GYR   e) hungry

i)

ii)

iii)

iv)

v)

2 Answer the questions. Then ask your friends.

a) Which is your favourite animal in the story? Why?

Buck because he's funny and clever.

b) Which animal don't you like? Why not?

Rudy because he's mean.

29

3 **Look at the animals. Complete the sentences with the words in the box.**

animals   fly   lived many years ago   eggs

a) These animals can
fly .

c) These animals
lived many years ago.

b) These animals have
eggs .

d) These animals eat other
animals .

4 **Look at the parts of the body. Write the names of the animals they come from.**

possum   mammoth   sloth   tiger   dinosaur

a) **mammoth**

b) *sloth*

c) *sabre tooth*

d) *dinosaur*

e) *possum*

Imagine...

1 Work in pairs. Choose one of these pictures
from the story.

2 Say a sentence. Your friend guesses the picture.

Chant

1  Listen and read.

Sid's song
I'm not frightened of mammoths,
Or weasels, or eggs,
But I'm very frightened of dinosaurs,
And the big T-Rex!

I'm not frightened of possums,
Or tigers or ice,
But I'm very frightened of Rudy,
He isn't very nice!

2 Say the chant.